THIS
BEN 10
ULTIMATE ALIEN
ANNUAL
BELONGS TO

# BEN 10 ULTIMATE ALIEN™

# CONTENTS




EGMONT

*We bring stories to life*

First published in Great Britain 2011 by Egmont UK Limited
239 Kensington High Street, London W8 6SA
Text by Laura Milne, Design by Ant Duke





ISBN 978 1 4052 5710 7
1 3 5 7 9 10 8 6 4 2
Printed in Italy

# ULTIMATE BEN 10

There's a time to go alien, and there's a time to go

***ULTIMATE ...***

**Ben 10** is back, but this time his secret is out and he's a world-famous superstar. He's also got more alien forms with more incredible powers than ever before! The Omnitrix has been destroyed and in its place is the awesome **Ultimatrix** – a device that allows **Ben** to turn into brand new aliens as well as transforming into 'ultimate' versions of existing alien dudes.

With evil villains still threatening Earth and the need to find and help five aliens that have been kidnapped by the evil **Aggregor**, **Ben's** going to be busy. So it's a good job that he still has **Gwen** and **Kevin** by his side.

Join **Ben** as he gets to grips with his new alien forms and put your brain to the test with the puzzles and quizzes inside!

**FIND NANOMECH**

He's tiny, but there are 10 hidden pictures of Nanomech like this one throughout the book. Can you find them all?

All answers are on pages 68 and 69.

**LET'S GO ULTIMATE!**

# BEN TENNYSON

Ben is now 16 years old, and trying not to let international fame go to his head! It's lucky his girlfriend, Julie, helps keep his feet on the ground.

HERO

BEN FACTS

- Ben now drives and has his own set of wheels – a cool green and black car.
- He's still at high-school and has to juggle his alien life with everyday studying.
- He now has a whole heap of brand new alien forms to master.

# THE ULTIMATRIX

The Ultimatrix is an upgraded form of the Omnitrix. It not only gives Ben access to all of his original powers and abilities, but also lets him evolve his alien forms into even stronger and more powerful ultimate versions! The watch can also scan and store the DNA of any alien that is not already held within it.

# GWEN TENNYSON

Gwen is Ben's 16 year-old cousin. She has some amazing powers of her own, and they come in really handy when helping Ben fight the bad guys.

**GWEN FACTS**

- Gwen's grandma is an Anodite – an alien.
- Brave and full of energy, Gwen is also the brains of the gang.
- She can control magical beams, platforms and orbs.

# ANODITE

Gwen was amazed to discover that her grandma is an Anodite – an alien. She had the chance to join her on the planet of Anodyne and learn how to master life energy, but she opted to stay on Earth with her friends and family and continue helping Ben.

# KEVIN LEVIN

The son of a former Plumber (an intergalactic policeman), 17 year-old Kevin is tough and loves to get stuck in. He's mastered his own absorbing powers and is also Gwen's boyfriend.

**KEVIN FACTS**

- He used to be one of the bad guys, so he knows how they tick.
- Kevin knows about illegal alien technology, as he used to trade in it.
- He can absorb any solid material, like stone, wood or steel.

HERO

# RUSTBUCKET III

The Rustbucket III is a very cool plane and spaceship. It belongs to Grandpa Max and it was a standard Plumber-issue ship, before Kevin made some improvements to it. After his car, the Rustbucket III is Kevin's pride and joy!

# GRANDPA MAX

Max Tennyson is Ben and Gwen's Grandpa. He's a retired member of the Plumbers (the intergalactic police force) and is tough, brave and loyal. Max is always on hand to provide advice for the gang.

"At first I thought the attacks were random. I was wrong. They're organised."

# JULIE YAMAMOTO

Julie is Ben's girlfriend. She thinks it's really cool that Ben can turn into aliens, and is pretty patient with him when he disappears to fight the bad guys. Julie's really bright, and she's also a talented tennis player.

# ULTIMATE BIG CHILL

Ultimate Big Chill can fly, turn invisible and create and shoot ice flames – which burn and then freeze the enemy.

## ALIEN FACTS

- Formed when Big Chill hits his Omnitrix symbol.
- Can breathe flames or shoot them from his hands.
- Is an even faster flyer than Big Chill.

HERO

## BIG CHILL

Big Chill is a flying ghost who can drop the temperature of anything he chooses to freezing point.

# FROZEN IN TIME

Ultimate Big Chill has been busy freezing the bad guys.
Can you spot 5 differences between these two pictures?

Answers on page 68.

# ULTIMATE CANNONBOLT

Ultimate Cannonbolt is covered in natural armour plating, including spikes. This armour protects him from almost any attack.

## ALIEN FACTS

- Formed when Cannonbolt hits his Omnitrix symbol.
- Can curl himself up into a ball to protect himself.
- As a ball, he can roll and spin towards enemies at high speeds.

HERO

## CANNONBOLT

Cannonbolt is a bulky alien whose body armour can protect him from acids, lasers and extreme heat.

# ROLL WITH IT

Show Ultimate Cannonbolt which way to roll through the maze, so that he can rescue Kevin. Make sure he knocks down all the Forever Knights as he goes!

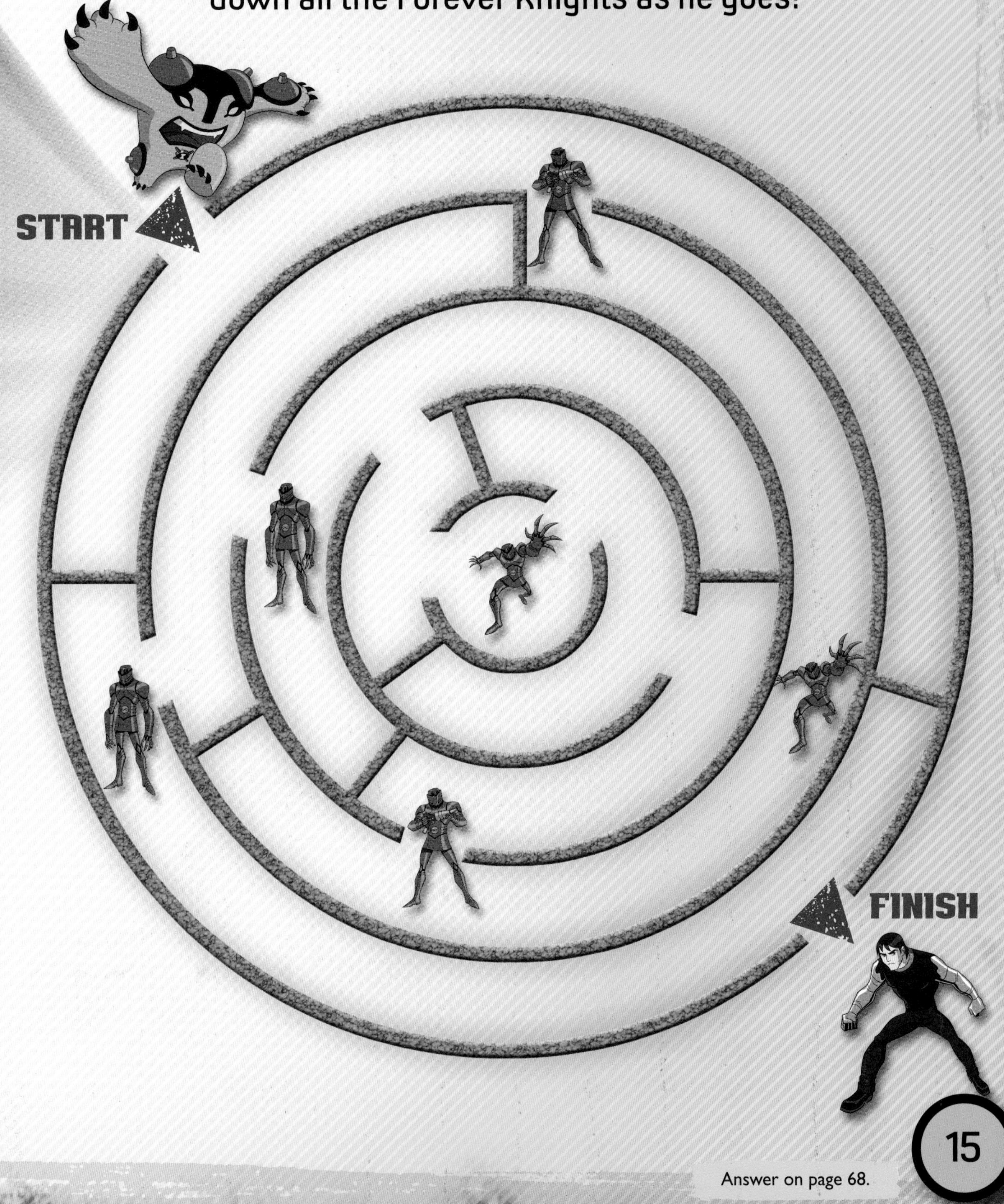


Answer on page 68.

# ULTIMATE ECHO ECHO

Ultimate Echo Echo has sonic powers which at full force can shatter steel. He can also fly!

ALIEN FACTS

- Formed when Echo Echo hits his Omnitrix symbol.
- By creating sonic booms, he becomes Ben's fastest flier.
- His body can send out floating discs as portable 'speakers' which amplify his sonic powers.

HERO

## ECHO ECHO

Echo Echo can project sonic waves and can also make exact copies of himself!

# THE REAL DEAL

Ultimate Echo Echo has some imposters. Only one of these pictures is the real hero. Can you find him?

Answer on page 68.

# ULTIMATE HUMUNGOUSAUR

Ultimate Humungousaur is bigger and stronger than ever before! He also has spikes on his body.

## ALIEN FACTS

- Formed when Humungousaur hits his Omnitrix symbol.
- Has blue armour and a slightly hunched back.
- Can fire missiles from his hands.

HERO

## HUMUNGOUSAUR

Humungousaur's thick dinosaur-skin protects him from most attacks.

# HUMUNGO-SEARCH

Ultimate Humungousaur is looking for some good and bad guys. Look for all the names in this grid. They can read up, down, across, backwards and diagonally.

| | | | | | | | | | | | | | |
|---|---|---|---|---|---|---|---|---|---|---|---|---|---|
| F | O | R | E | V | E | R | K | N | I | G | H | T | S |
| R | U | S | T | B | R | T | A | E | T | H | E | T | I |
| W | T | F | M | X | T | L | U | L | M | A | N | J | S |
| I | J | D | C | T | K | L | M | O | S | G | N | J | E |
| L | B | J | U | L | I | E | Z | D | S | G | F | A | M |
| L | T | A | L | C | N | O | K | T | S | R | G | H | E |
| H | F | U | T | N | B | J | G | O | E | E | M | G | N |
| A | L | T | V | M | D | E | W | T | R | G | A | A | N |
| R | O | J | O | C | K | P | E | U | P | O | X | J | I |
| A | S | Z | T | K | M | N | N | X | E | R | U | K | A |
| N | A | C | K | E | V | I | N | B | N | D | F | H | T |
| G | C | H | A | R | M | C | A | S | T | E | R | E | P |
| U | T | C | A | T | D | V | A | E | D | M | A | L | A |
| E | C | S | E | V | E | N | S | E | V | E | N | T | C |

FOREVER KNIGHTS
MAX
WILL HARANGUE
AGGREGOR
SEVEN SEVEN
ROJO
KEVIN
GWEN
ZOMBOZO
SSSERPENT
CAPTAIN NEMESIS
JULIE
CHARMCASTER



Answers on page 68.

# ULTIMATE SPIDERMONKEY

Ultimate Spidermonkey looks like an ape with very long spider legs! Like any real ape, he is immensely strong.

ALIEN FACTS

- Formed when Spidermonkey hits his Omnitrix symbol.
- He can shoot webs with his mouth.
- He has super strength.

HERO

## SPIDERMONKEY

Spidermonkey is a super-agile six-limbed alien who can shoot webs from his tail.

# WEB TRAP

Ultimate Spidermonkey has shot some webs to trap a villain. Follow the trails to work out which one leads to the bad guy. Do you know who the villain is? Write his name on the dotted line.

The villain is a _ _ _ _ _ _ _ _ _ / _ _ _ _ _ _ _ _



Answers on page 68.

# ULTIMATE SWAMPFIRE

Ultimate Swampfire's armour is made from bark and it contains little sacks of organic napalm! The flames he produces are blue and hotter than ever.

## ALIEN FACTS

- Formed when Swampfire hits his Omnitrix symbol.
- He can control plants and re-grow body parts.
- The flames he makes are like fire bombs.



## SWAMPFIRE

Swampfire can shoot out flames, regenerate severed limbs and create a highly flammable gas.

# TOTALLY SWAMPED

Things are heating up! Count how many pictures there are of Swampfire and Ultimate Swampfire and fill in the answers below.

SWAMPFIRE ☐ ULTIMATE SWAMPFIRE ☐

Answers on page 68.

# TABLOID TROUBLE

Written by JAKE BLACK, art by MIN S KU,
Colours by HEROIC AGE, letters by TRAVIS LANHAM,
Edits by SEAN RYAN, BEN 10 ULTIMATE ALIEN
created by Man of Action

THAT? IT'S NOT A BIG DEAL, JULIE. IT'S JUST THE TABLOIDS SPREADING THEIR GOSSIP. HAPPENS ALL THE TIME.
DONUTS
POP

NOT TO ME IT DOESN'T!

YOU LIVE IN THE SPOTLIGHT, YOU'RE GOING TO BE SEEN.

I DON'T *WANT* TO BE IN THE SPOTLIGHT. I JUST NEED A MINUTE.

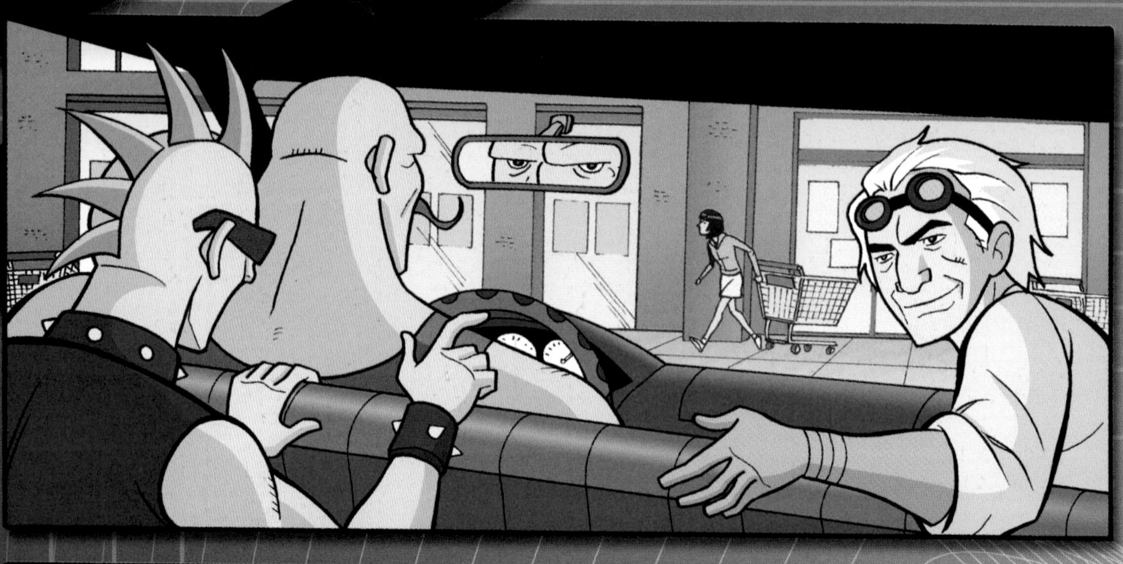

DON'T YOU GET IT, BEN? I WANT OUR RELATIONSHIP TO STILL BE PRIVATE.
HIGH's
NISSN

YOU'RE COMING WITH US.

BEN! HELP!

Megan's
JULIE, IT'S REALLY NOTHING TO WORRY ABOUT...

Price-Co
JULIE?!
Banas Crunch
oats 4 me

SODA pop

I'LL SAVE YOU.

I CAN'T BELIEVE I LOST THEIR CAR IN THIS TRAFFIC!
DON'T BE SCARED, JULIE.
I NEED TO THINK. FIGURE OUT MY PLAN.
BREEEP BREEEP
JULIE?
10

NOT JULIE, TENNYSON. BUT SHE'S HERE.
LET HER GO.
OH, WE WILL. BUT NOT UNTIL YOU GIVE US THE ULTIMATRIX.
YOU'RE CRAZY.
MAYBE, BUT THAT'S THE DEAL.
IF YOU WANT YOUR LITTLE GIRLFRIEND BACK, BRING THE ULTIMATRIX TO THE DOCKS, PIER SIX, AT MIDNIGHT.
AND COME ALONE.
WHAT OTHER CHOICE DO I HAVE?

MIDNIGHT.
YOU BRING THE ULTIMATRIX?
IT'S HERE. LET HER GO.
I'M A MAN OF MY WORD, TENNYSON. PUT THE ULTIMATRIX ON THE GROUND, AND YOU CAN HAVE YOUR GIRL BACK.
BUZZ
BUZZ

YES!

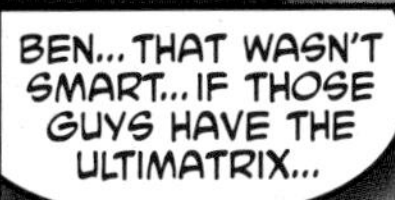
BEN... THAT WASN'T SMART... IF THOSE GUYS HAVE THE ULTIMATRIX...

WE WON! THE WORLD IS GOING TO BE OURS!

SHHHHH.
10

MAKE ME AN ALIEN!

MAYBE IT'S BROKEN.
UH... GUYS... LOOK...

I CAN'T BELIEVE YOU FELL FOR THAT!
THAT WAS A FAKE ULTIMATRIX... A TOY!
I'M THE REAL DEAL.
BUZZ
WE'RE NOT SCARED OF YOU. IT'S THREE AGAINST ONE.
BOO.
LET'S GET OUTTA HERE!

SHOULDN'T YOU CATCH THEM?
I TOLD THE POLICE WHERE THEY WERE BEFORE I CAME. THERE'S A SWAT TEAM WAITING FOR THEM RIGHT OVER THERE.
I'M SORRY OUR RELATIONSHIP IS SO PUBLIC. IT MADE YOU A TARGET.
IT'S OKAY, BEN. A SUPER HERO'S GIRLFRIEND IS ALWAYS IN HARM'S WAY.
BUT IT'S WORTH IT. YOU'RE WORTH IT.
AS LONG AS YOU SAVE ME EVERY TIME!
COUNT ON IT!
the End

# THE VILLAINS

Ever since the world found out about Ben's powers, a lot of his old enemies have been crawling out of the woodwork. Here are just a few of them. But there's also one major new threat out there ...

## AGGREGOR

is the main villain in Ultimate Alien. He is mysterious and has absorbing powers. He kidnapped five aliens (Bivalvan, Andreas, P'andor, Ra'ad and Galapagus) from the Andromeda Galaxy, but they escaped from his ship to Earth. Now Aggregor is hunting them down one by one. He wants to drain the aliens' powers and claim what he calls 'the ultimate prize'.

VILLAIN

# FOREVER KNIGHTS

Ben first met the Forever Knights in Alien Force. They are a secret society formed during the Middle Ages and they seek alien technology for their own use. They wear a full suit of metal body armour.

VILLAIN

# WILL HARANGUE

Will Harangue is a wealthy and power-crazy TV presenter. He's jealous of Ben's fame and sees him as a menace, not a superhero.

# CAPTAIN NEMESIS

Captain Nemesis used to be a superhero and Ben was one of his biggest fans. But Nemesis' fame has corrupted him, and now he's all bad. He is very strong, able to fly with a jet pack and he can boost up his suit with devastating results.

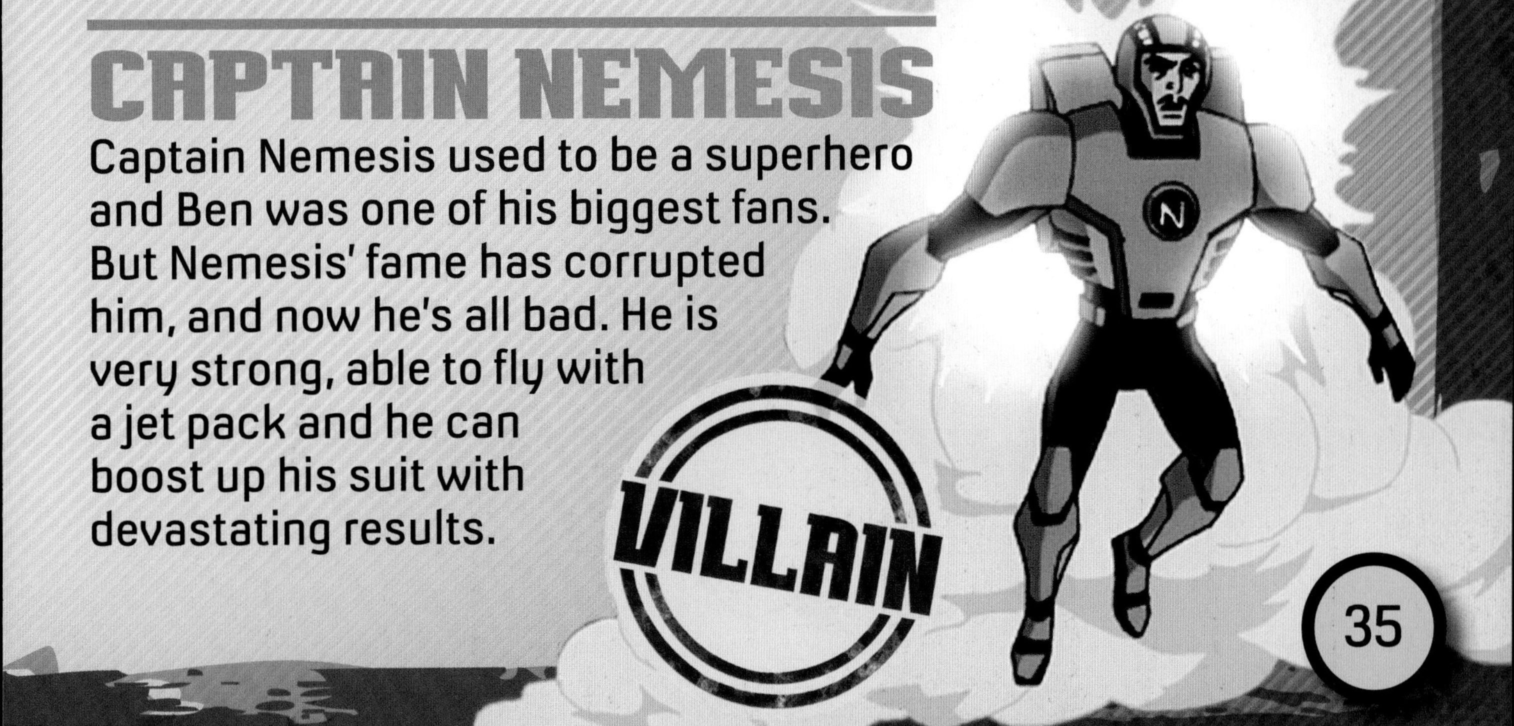

## ZOMBOZO

Ben first met Zombozo six years ago and he's back to cause more trouble. He's a scary clown with plenty of tricks up his sleeve, including a trick buzzer that stuns his victims. Zombozo often teams up with Charmcaster and Vulkanus.

## CHARMCASTER

Charmcaster is a witch who Ben and Gwen came up against when they were younger. Now she's back and has a team of lumbering rock monsters under her control. Charmcaster can also scatter strange seeds which quickly sprout into huge vines.

VILLAIN

## VULKANUS

The gang first met Vulkanus long ago. He's an alien technology dealer who has lots of blaster weapons. He looks huge in his robotic, hi-tech suit – but really he's just a tiny orange alien beneath all that bulky armour!

VILLAIN

# WHAT NEXT?

Ben's come face-to-face with Ssserpent, a creepy half-man, half-cobra creature. Use this space to draw what you think happens next. Be sure to choose a powerful alien transformation for Ben!

# ARMODRILLO

Armodrillo is a bulky robotic alien with drills in his arms. The tremors he creates can cause earthquakes, and he can move easily through solid rock.

## ALIEN FACTS

- Can drill into the earth using his very strong arms.
- His main form of attack is a powerful 'pneumatic drill' punch.
- He was created when the Ultimatrix scanned an alien called Andreas.

# ARMODRILLO ACTION

Armodrillo's been scaring off some Forever Knights. The picture has broken up – can you help put it back together again? Work out which pieces are missing, then draw lines to match them up.

Answers on page 68.

# NANOMECH

Nanomech is a tiny carbon-based life form. He is small enough to enter machines! But he packs a powerful punch by firing out powerful energy bolts.

## ALIEN FACTS

- Can become tiny and shrink to sub-atomic particle size.
- This little guy is able to fly.
- He comes from a hive of insects, but is human in shape.

HERO

# NANOMECH COLOUR

Colour in Nanomech to bring him to life!

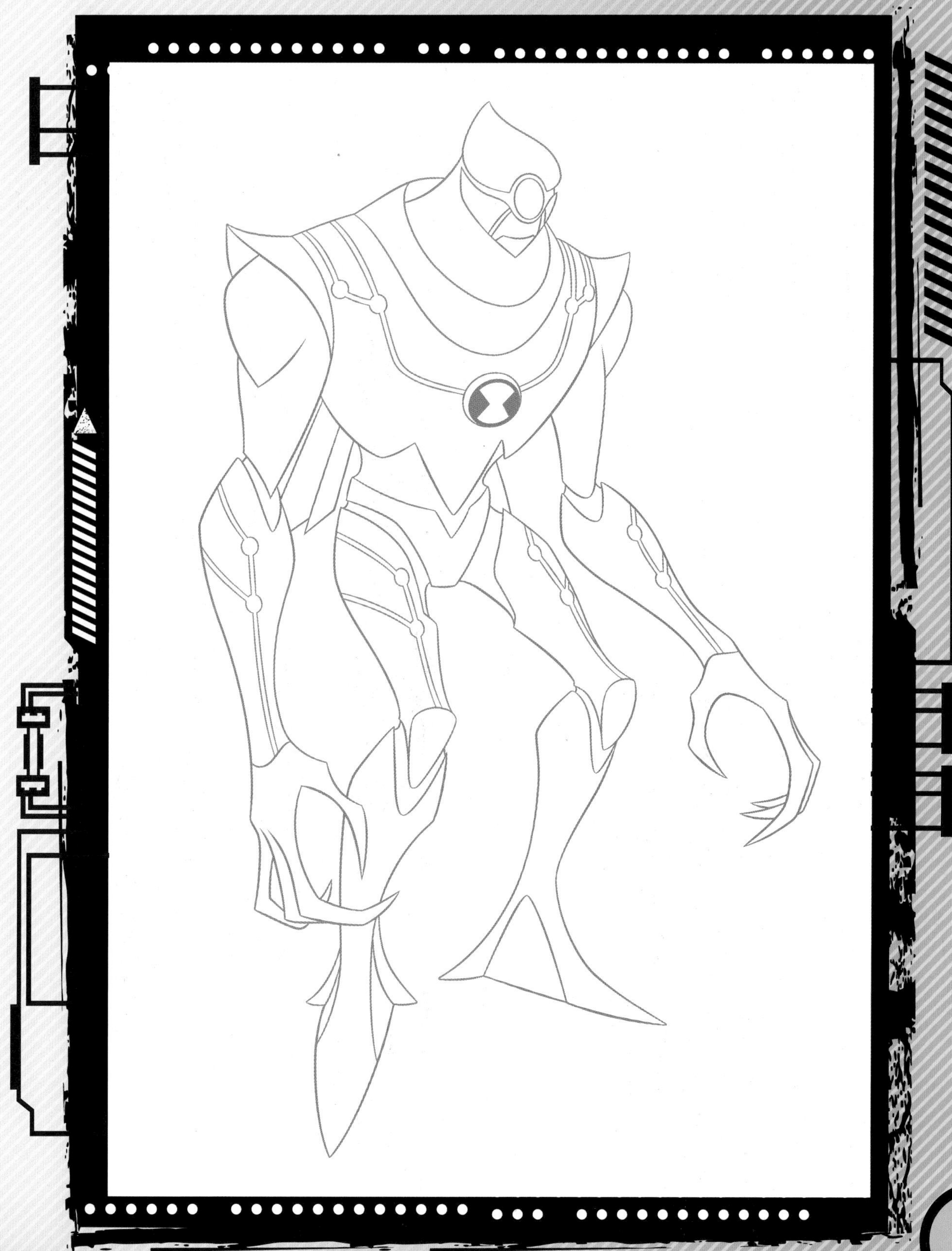

# NRG

NRG is a radioactive energy life-form contained in the toughest armour. He has heat-based powers that allow him to melt through solid metal and rock.

# NRG BLASTS

NRG fires 6 energy blasts at some Forever Knights.
Use the coordinates grid to work out which Knights he hits.
(The Knight in coordinate A3 has already been knocked out.)

Coordinates: B5 D5 B2 D3 C4 E4

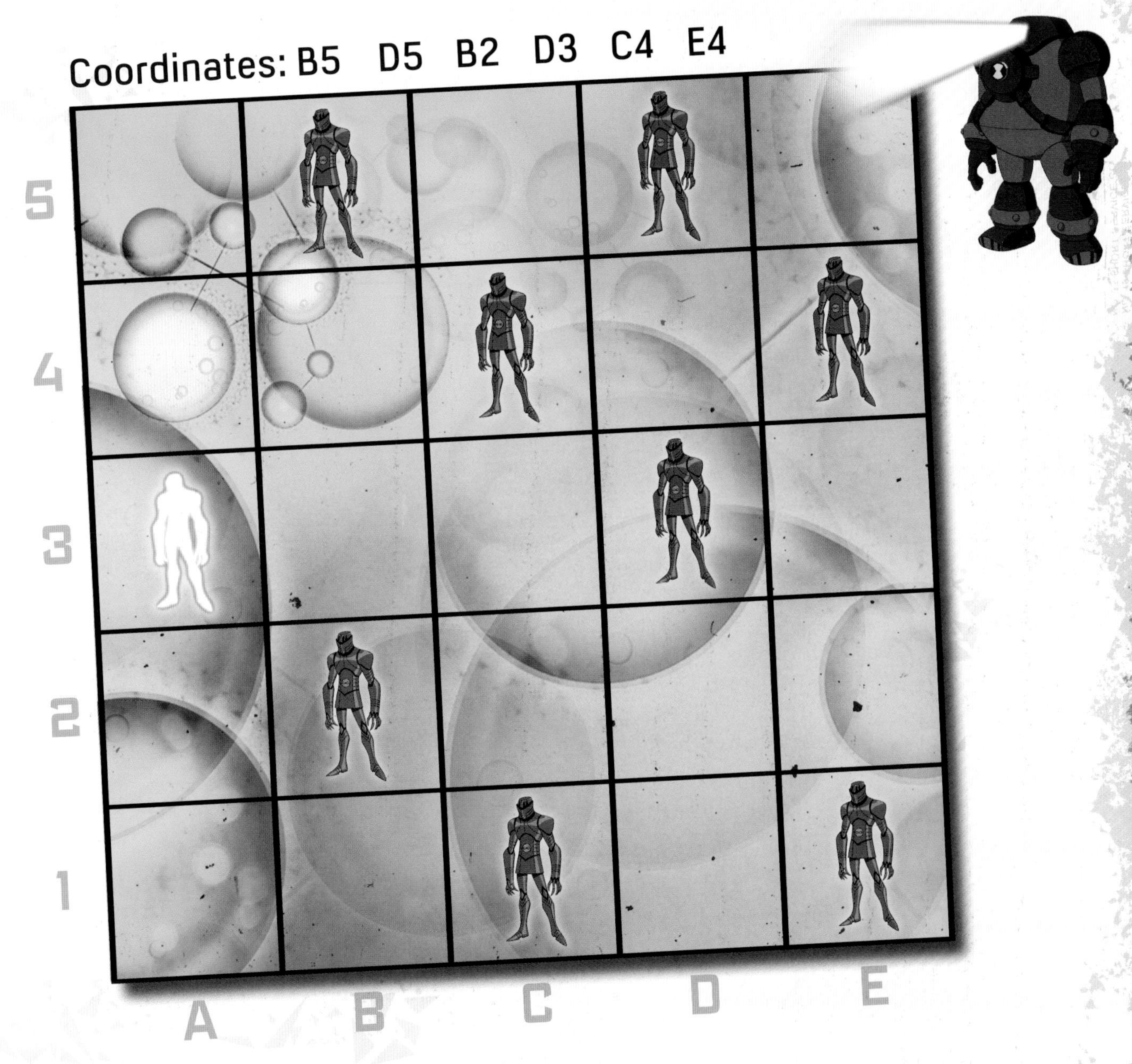


**How many Forever Knights are left?**

**There are ◯ left, in coordinates ◯ .**



Answers on page 69.

# TERRASPIN

Terraspin is a turtle-like alien. He can shrink his head into his shell and blow wind through the holes in his shell to fly!

ALIEN FACTS

- Can generate gale force winds.
- He uses his fins to spin at high speed and attack bad guys!
- He was created when the Ultimatrix scanned an alien called Galapagus.

HERO

# TERRASPIN'S GRID

Terraspin's feeling a bit dizzy. Can you help him complete this puzzle? See if you can fit the words in the grid below. One has been done for you.

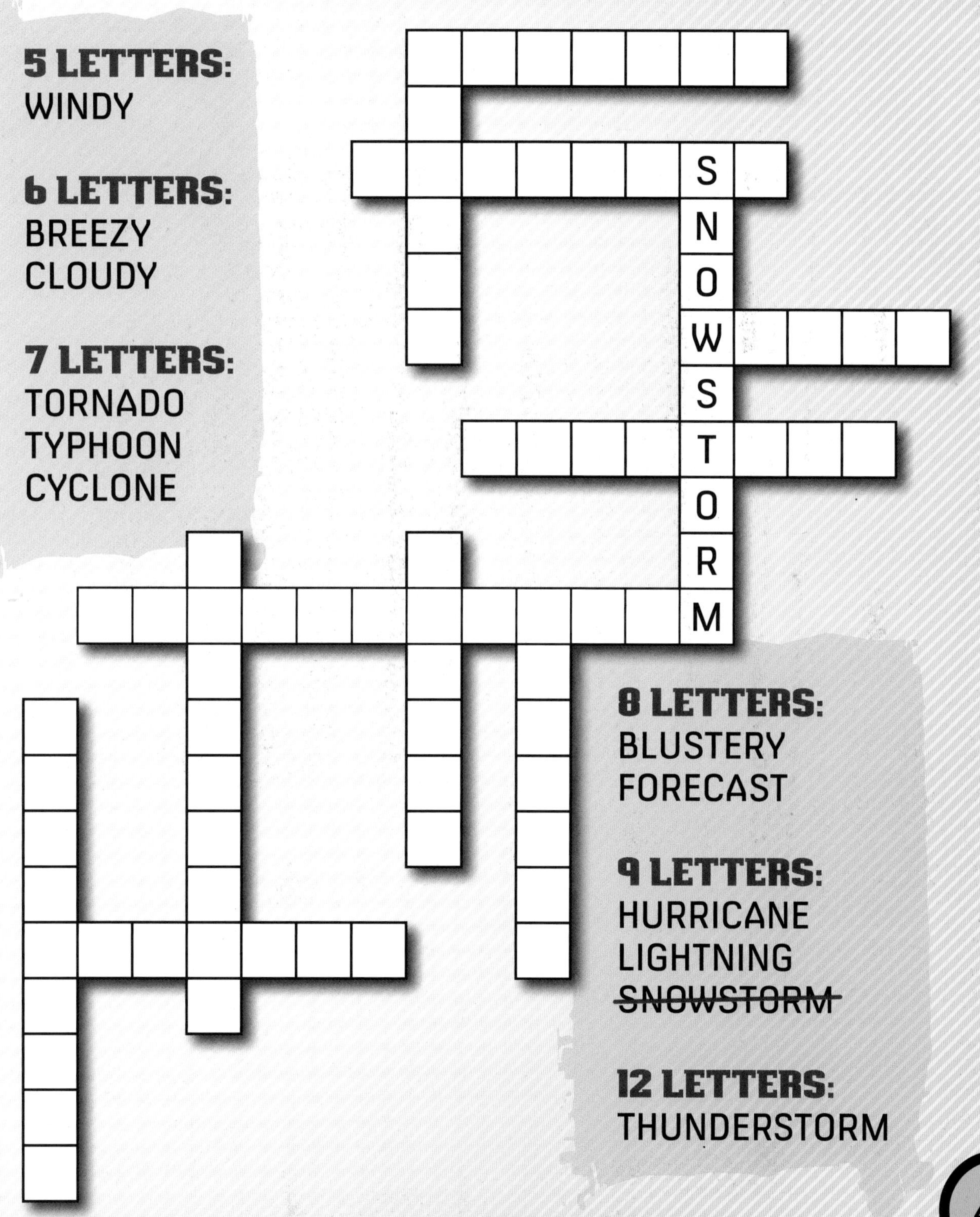


**5 LETTERS:**
WINDY

**6 LETTERS:**
BREEZY
CLOUDY

**7 LETTERS:**
TORNADO
TYPHOON
CYCLONE

**8 LETTERS:**
BLUSTERY
FORECAST

**9 LETTERS:**
HURRICANE
LIGHTNING
~~SNOWSTORM~~

**12 LETTERS:**
THUNDERSTORM

Answers on page 69.

Water Hazard looks a bit like a crab. He's able to breathe underwater and can shoot highly-pressurized water blasts from his palms.

**ALIEN FACTS**

- Can control water and mould it into all sorts of shapes.
- His armour-like body is extremely tough.
- He was created when the Ultimatrix scanned an alien called Bivalvan.

Which of Water Hazard's water blasts will knock Aggregor out? The most powerful route is the one with the largest total when the numbers are added together. Write the totals for each route in the spaces at the bottom.

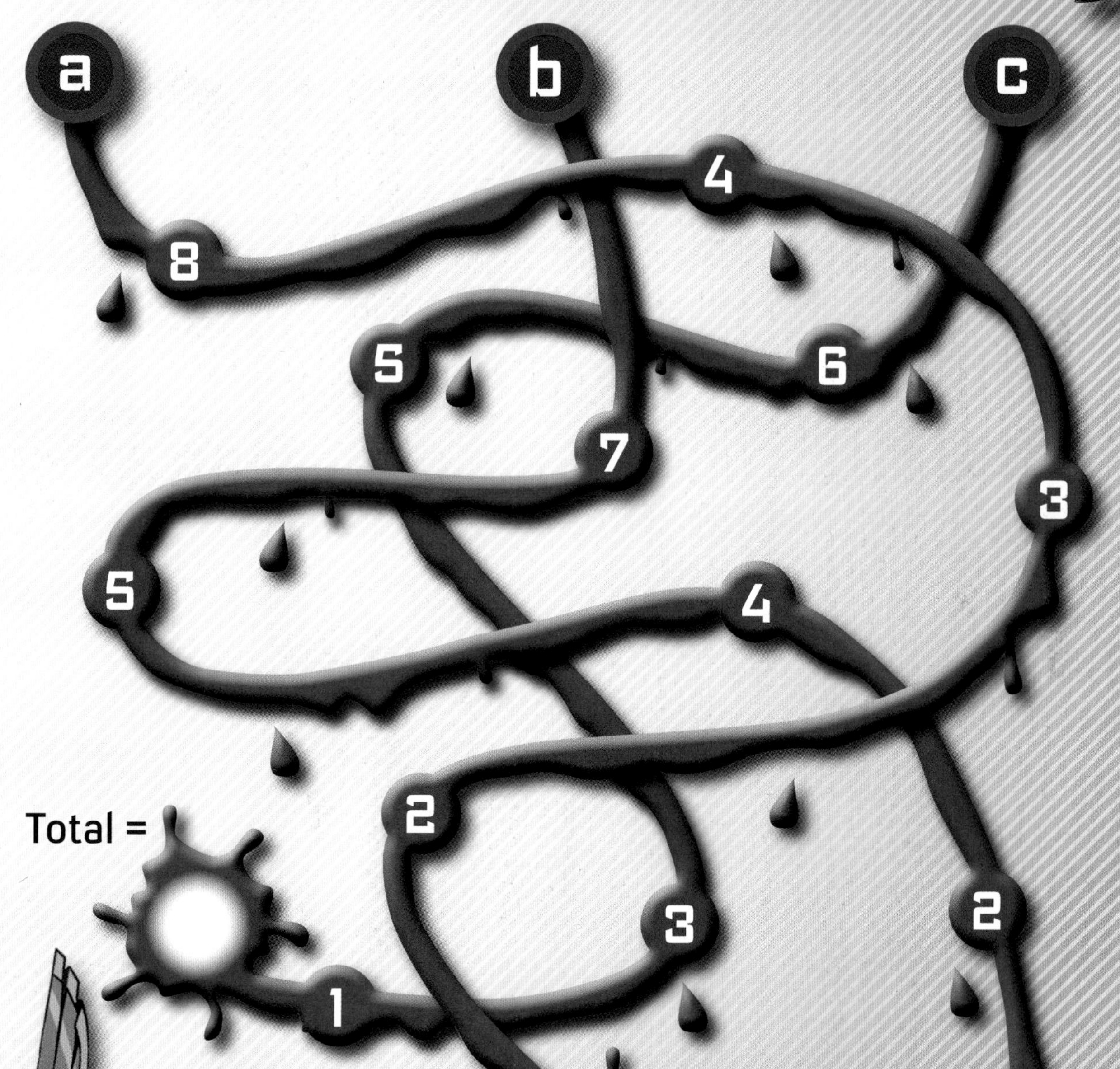


Answers on page 69.

# STAR CHASER

MAN, AFTER A DAY LIKE THAT, I'LL BE GLAD TO GET HOME!

KINDA WISH THE FOREVER KNIGHTS HADN'T PUT KEVIN'S CAR IN THE SHOP AGAIN. COULD HAVE USED THE RIDE.

**Written by JAKE BLACK, art by ETHAN BEAVERS,
Colours by HEROIC AGE, letters by DC, Edits by SEAN RYAN,
BEN 10 ULTIMATE ALIEN created by Man of Action**

SOUNDS LIKE SOMEONE'S FOLLOWING ME.

RELAX, BEN. YOU'RE BEING OVERLY PARANOID.
IT'S NOT LIKE IT'S VILGAX OR SOMETHING.
ELSIE
SMU UNIVERSITY
WAIT. MAYBE I'M NOT AS PARANOID AS I THOUGHT.

Kaietlyn's Books
THIS DOESN'T LOOK GOOD.
YOU WANT A FIGHT...
...THEN LET'S FIGHT.

WHERE ARE YOU? SHOW YOURSELF!
I'M DOWN HERE.
MISTER... UH... TENNYSON... CAN I HAVE YOUR AUTOGRAPH?
OH, YEAH, OF COURSE.
I THOUGHT YOU WERE A BIG, BAD GUY!
TEE HEE. NOPE...
I LIKE HER A LOT MORE THAN THE BIG, BAD GUYS.
THE END

# LODESTAR

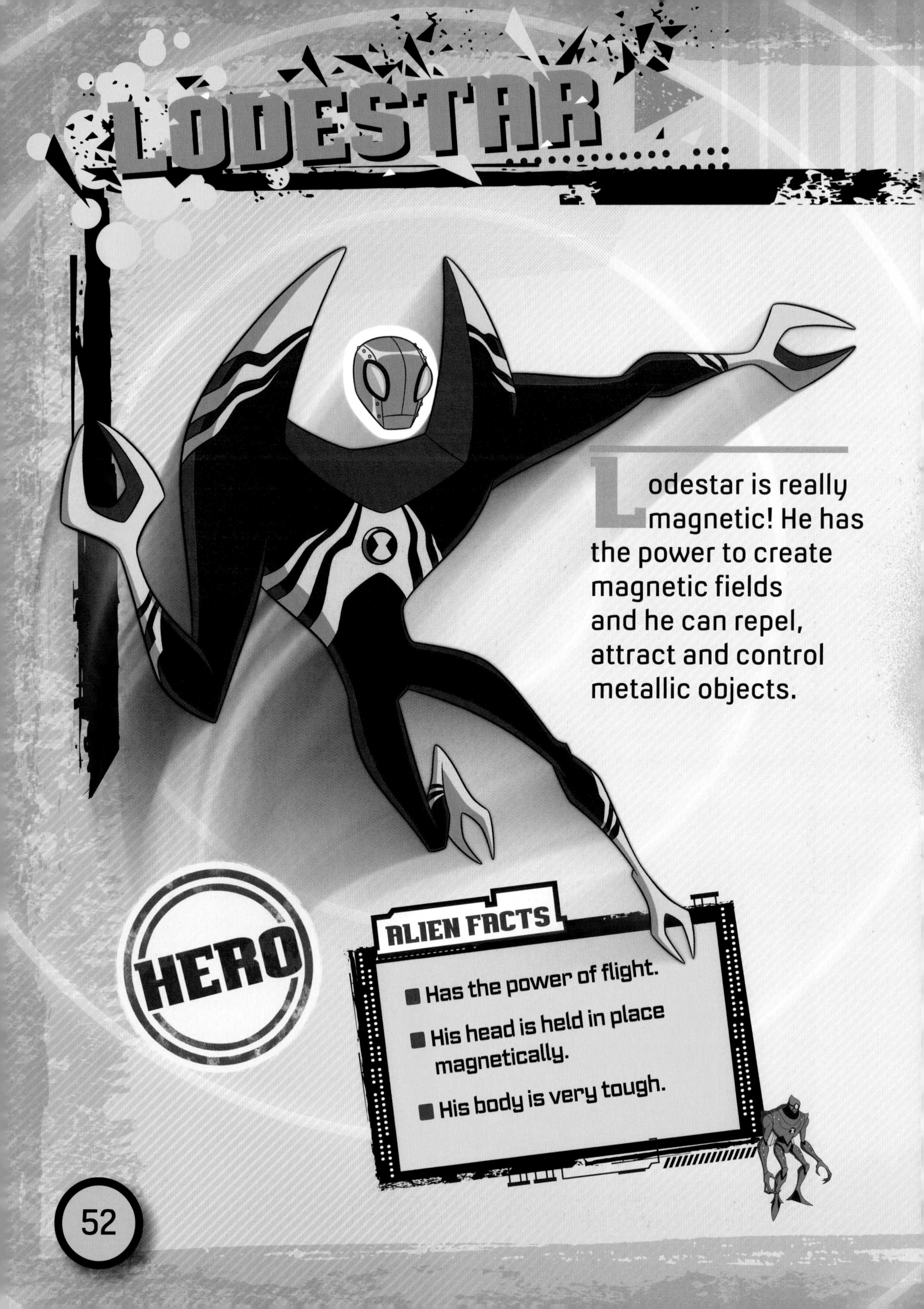


Lodestar is really magnetic! He has the power to create magnetic fields and he can repel, attract and control metallic objects.

**ALIEN FACTS**

- Has the power of flight.
- His head is held in place magnetically.
- His body is very tough.

# MAGNETIC ART

Bring Lodestar to life by colouring him in!

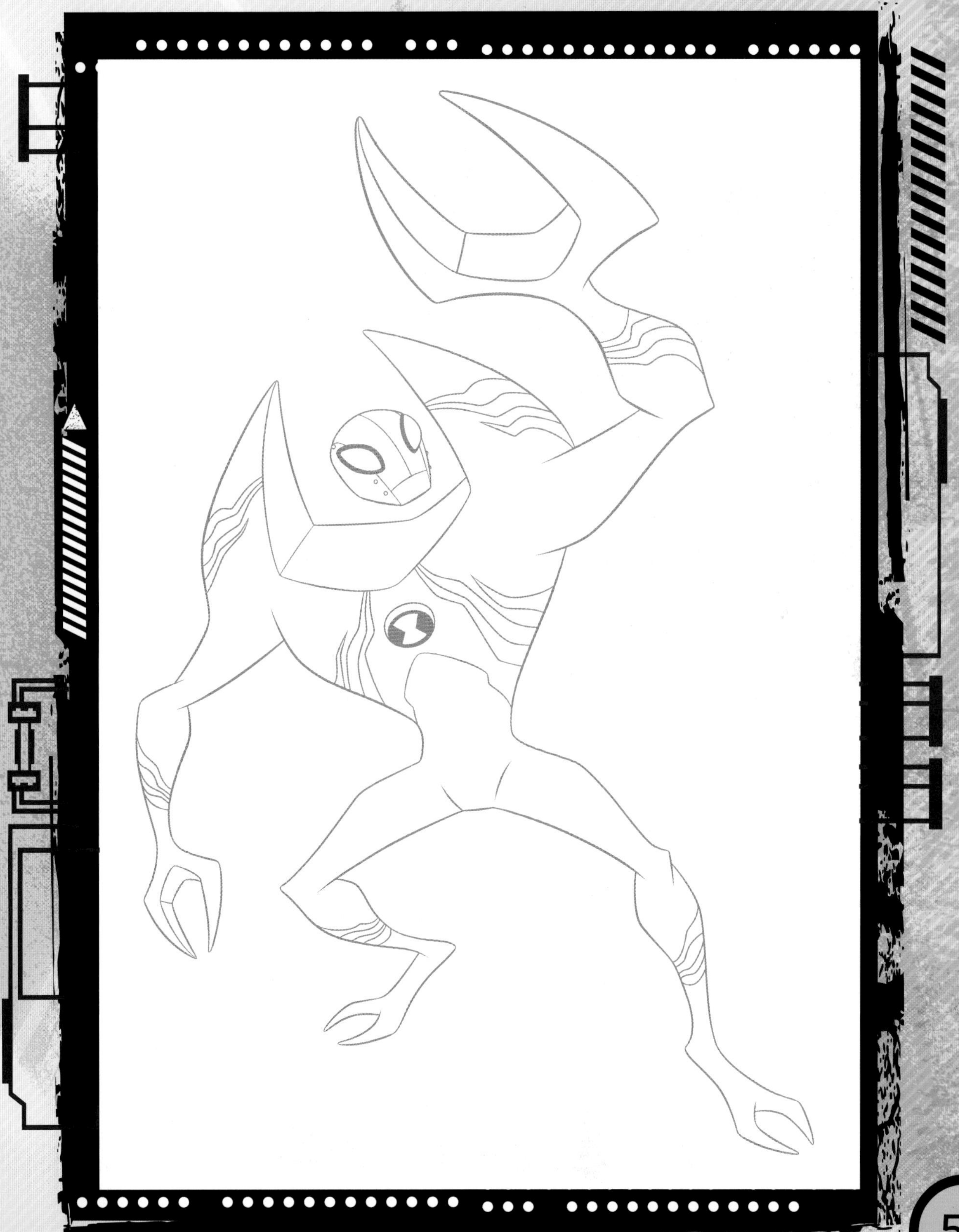

# RATH

Rath is like a boxer and is Ben's angriest alien! He is also very powerful and has a razor-sharp claw on each hand.

# RATH'S SPEECH

Rath's being snarly! He's saying something, but it's all in code. Use the code breaker to work out what he's saying.

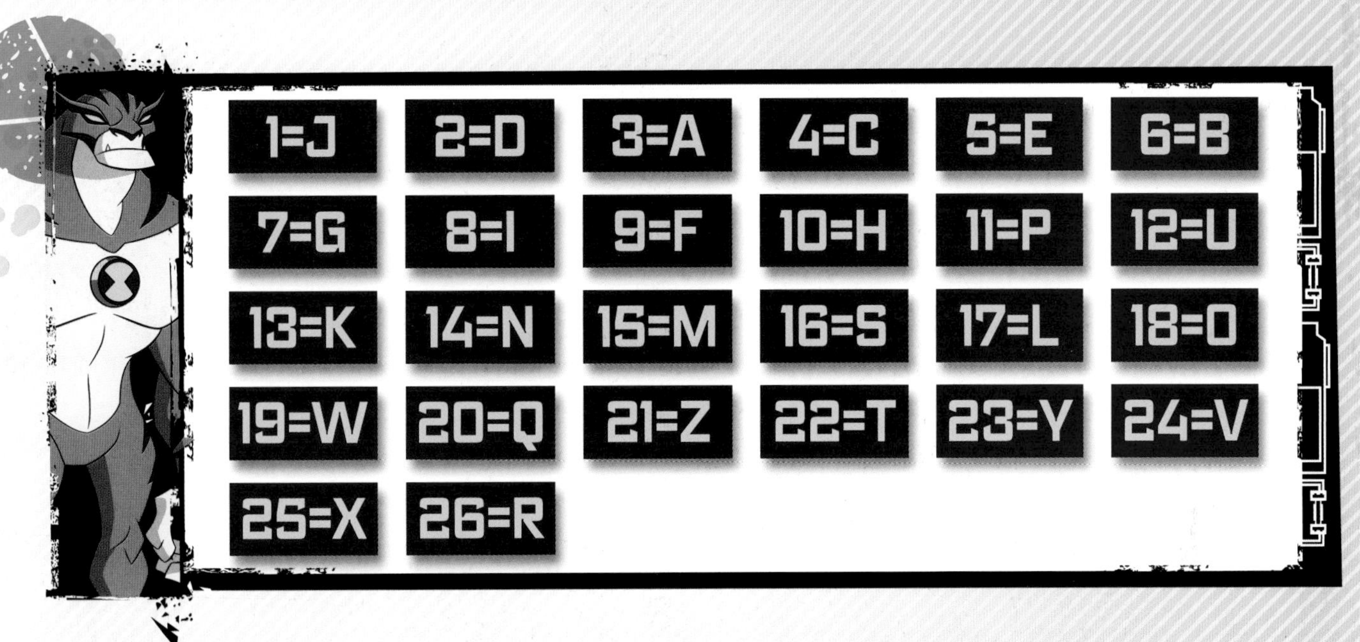

| | | | | | |
|---|---|---|---|---|---|
| 1=J | 2=D | 3=A | 4=C | 5=E | 6=B |
| 7=G | 8=I | 9=F | 10=H | 11=P | 12=U |
| 13=K | 14=N | 15=M | 16=S | 17=L | 18=O |
| 19=W | 20=Q | 21=Z | 22=T | 23=Y | 24=V |
| 25=X | 26=R | | | | |

**The code**

17 / 5 / 22   15 / 5   22 / 5 / 17 / 17   23 / 18 / 12

16 / 18 / 15 / 5 / 22 / 10 / 8 / 14 / 7 !

_ _ _   _ _   _ _ _ _   _ _ _

_ _ _ _ _ _ _ _ _ _ !

Answer on page 69.

# AMPFIBIAN

Ampfibian's powers are electric, but he's also a very fast swimmer who can breathe underwater. Jellyfish-like Ampfibian uses his long tendrils to zap victims.

## ALIEN FACTS

- He can drain electricity from objects.
- He's able to travel as electric current through power lines.
- He was created when the Ultimatrix scanned an alien called Ra'ad.

# AMPFIBI-MATCH

Take a look at these scenes. Which two environments do you think Ampfibian would be best suited to? Draw lines to match Ampfibian to them.

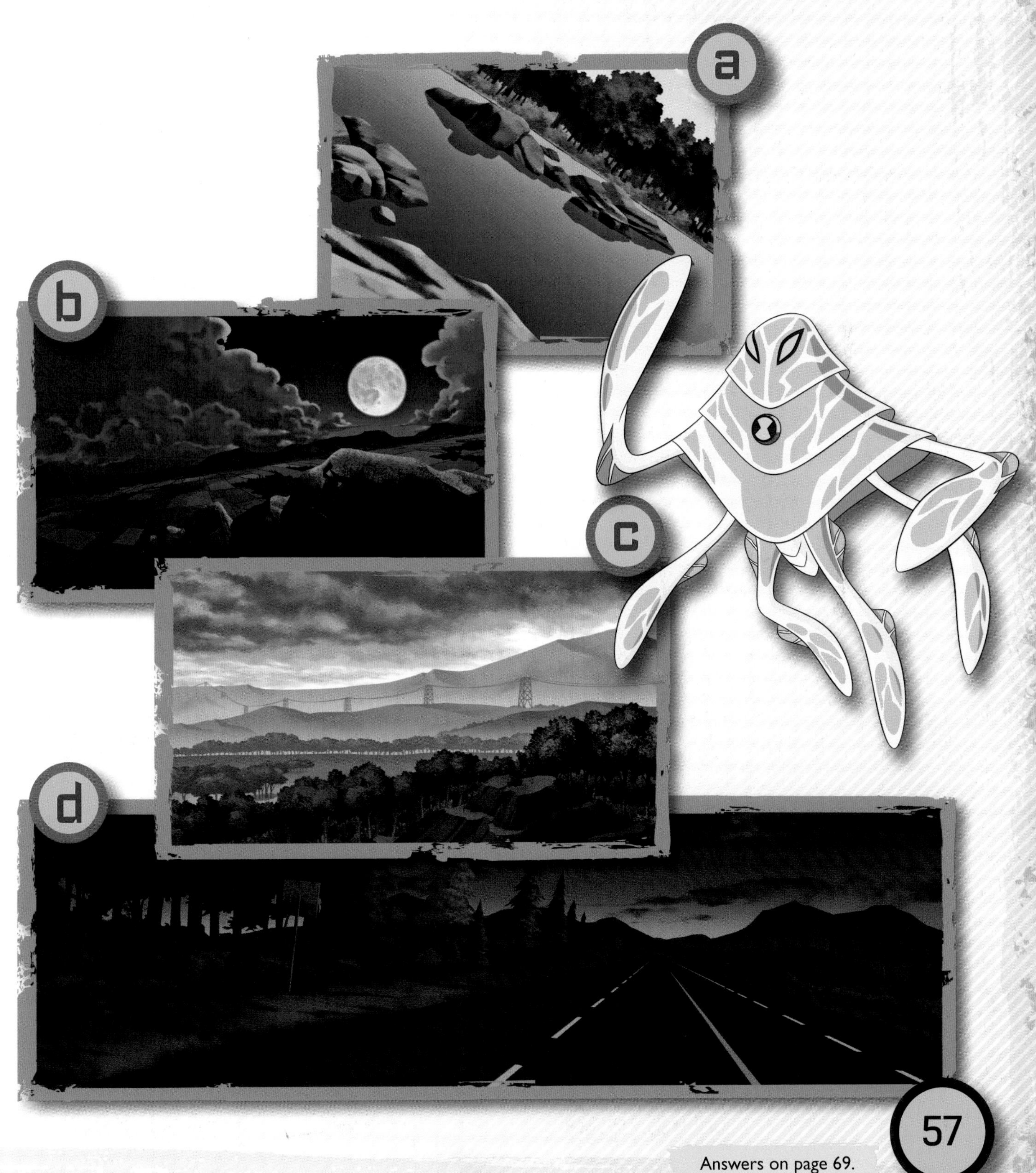




Answers on page 69.

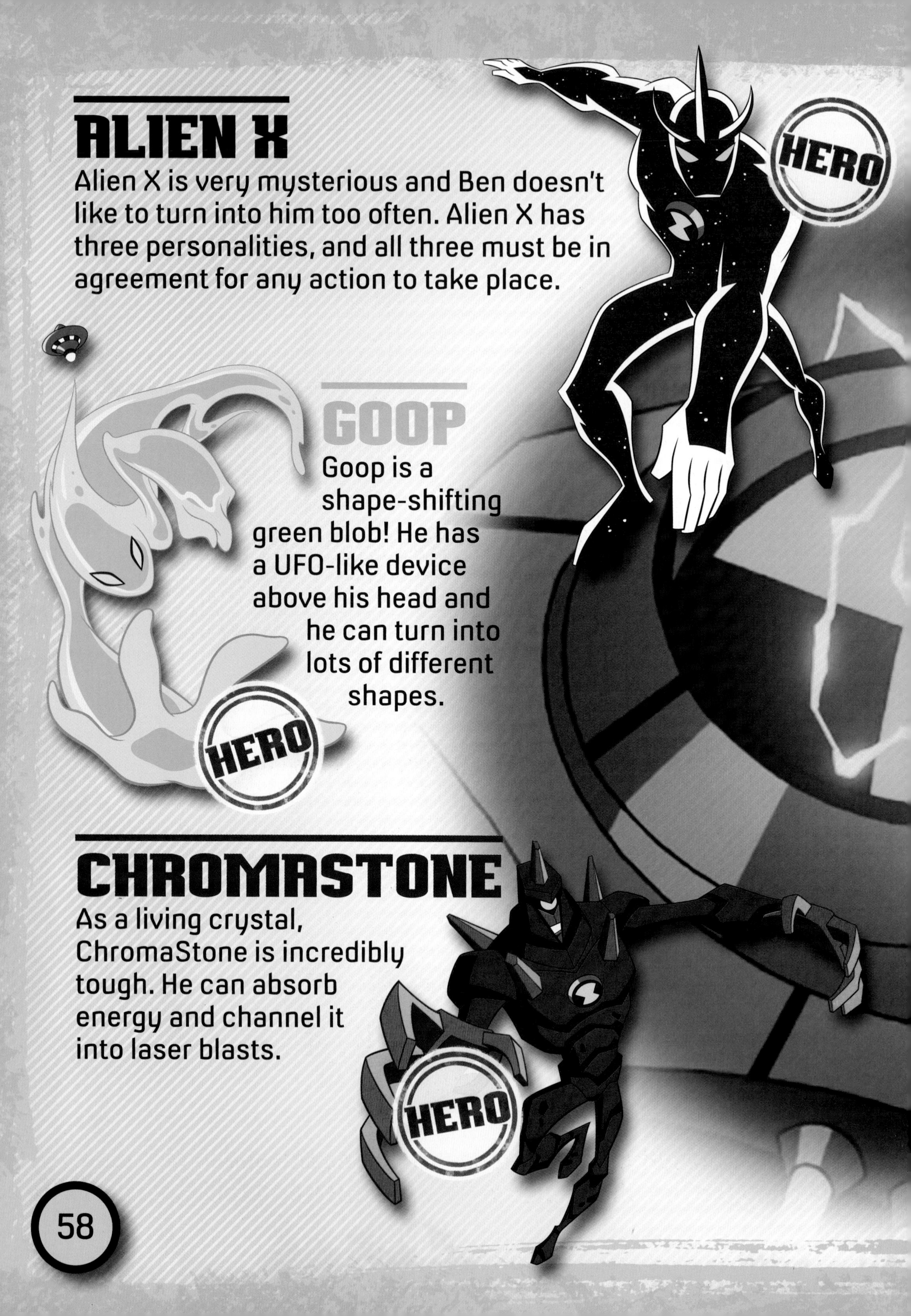


# ALIEN X

Alien X is very mysterious and Ben doesn't like to turn into him too often. Alien X has three personalities, and all three must be in agreement for any action to take place.

# GOOP

Goop is a shape-shifting green blob! He has a UFO-like device above his head and he can turn into lots of different shapes.

# CHROMASTONE

As a living crystal, ChromaStone is incredibly tough. He can absorb energy and channel it into laser blasts.

## DIAMONDHEAD

Diamondhead is one of Ben's original aliens from when he was 10. He can fire crystal shards and he can even re-grow lost limbs.

## BRAIN STORM

Brain Storm is Ben's cleverest alien transformation. He can produce electrical storms just by thinking hard enough.

## JET RAY

Jet Ray can swim and fly at several times the speed of sound. He can also fire shock blasts from his eyes and tail!

# DODGE BEN

I HATE DODGE BALL.
Written by JAKE BLACK,
art by ETHAN BEAVERS,
Colours by HEROIC AGE, letters by DC,
Edits by SEAN RYAN, BEN 10 ULTIMATE ALIEN
created by Man of Action

STAY CLOSE TO ME, JAMES. I WON'T LET THEM HIT YOU WITH THE BALL.
THANKS, BEN.

CHAMPIONS
SPARTANS
YOU GUYS ARE MINE!

BAM
OOOF!

CHAMPIONS
THANKS FOR TRYING, BEN.
WHO HIT ME?
DUSTIN. NEW KID.

I THINK I'M GOING TO LIKE IT HERE!

OW!
DUDE, THE GAME'S OVER!

CAN'T HIDE NOW, JAMES!
PLEASE, LEAVE ME ALONE.

THAT'S NOT RIGHT.

GIMME YOUR LUNCH MONEY!
N-NO. I'M GONNA GET A TEACHER.

LEAVE HIM ALONE.

WHO ARE YOU?
THAT'S BEN TENNYSON! *THE* BEN TENNYSON. YOU BETTER LISTEN TO HIM!
HIM? HE'S JUST A SQUIRT!

I SAID LET HIM GO!

YEAH! YOU BETTER RUN!

THANKS FOR SAVING ME, BEN.
IT'S WHAT I DO!
THE END

# ULTIMATE POWER!

Not all of Ben's aliens have Ultimate forms. If you could, which aliens would you turn Ultimate? Perhaps Armodrillo, Water Hazard or NRG ... Draw what you think it would look like, and write down what powers it would have.

# ALIEN SHADOWS

Can you tell which of Ben's aliens is which, from their shadows? Draw lines to match each alien shadow to its colour picture. Bonus points if you know the aliens' names!

Answers on page 69.

# ULTIMATE QUIZ

Here's a final quiz to test your Ben 10 know-how! You'll need to look back at other pages in the Annual to get some of the answers. Write your answers in the spaces. When you've got them all, take just the first letter of each word, and write them in the spaces at the bottom to help complete the missing word. You'll see that two letters are in place already.

1. This alien's body has detachable discs.

______________________

2. Turn to page 55. You need the first word in Rath's code.

______________________

3. Turn to page 45. You need the 12-letter word in Terraspin's Grid.

______________________

4. At the beginning of the story 'Tabloid Trouble', Ben and Julie are going to see a ...

______________________

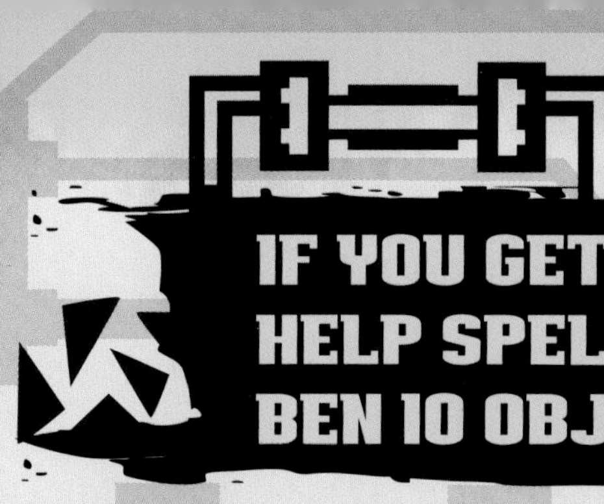

**IF YOU GET THEM ALL CORRECT, YOU'LL HELP SPELL THE NAME OF AN AWESOME BEN 10 OBJECT!**

5. The main villain in Ben 10 Ultimate Alien.

______________________________

6. This alien looks like a turtle.

______________________________

7. The name of the gang's flying transport.

______________________________

8. Ben's most mysterious alien is Alien ...

______________________________

_ _ _ I _ _ _ _ I _

# ANSWERS

## Page 7

FIND NANOMECH – The 10 hidden images of Nanomech are on pages 13, 17, 22, 30, 35, 42, 47, 52, 60 and 67

## Page 13

FROZEN IN TIME

## Page 15

ROLL WITH IT

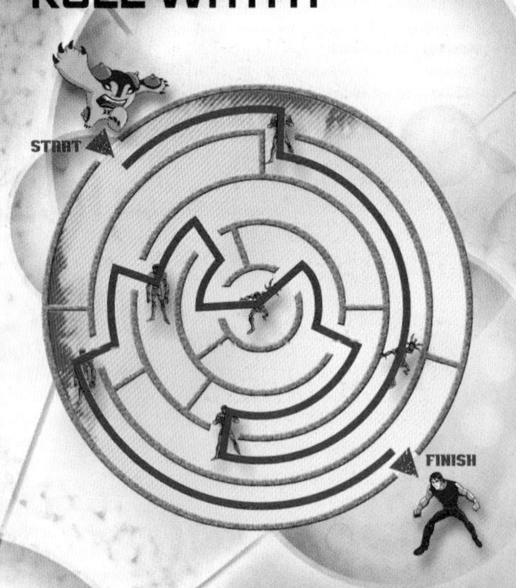


## Page 17

THE REAL DEAL – b is the real hero.

## Page 19

HUMUNGO-SEARCH

| F | O | R | E | V | E | R | K | N | I | G | H | T | S |
|---|---|---|---|---|---|---|---|---|---|---|---|---|---|
| R | U | S | T | B | R | T | A | E | T | H | E | T | I |
| W | T | F | M | X | T | L | U | L | M | A | N | J | S |
| I | J | D | C | T | K | L | M | O | S | G | N | J | E |
| L | B | J | U | L | I | E | Z | D | S | G | F | A | M |
| L | T | A | L | C | N | O | K | T | S | R | G | H | E |
| H | F | U | T | N | B | J | G | O | E | E | M | G | N |
| A | L | T | V | M | D | E | W | T | R | G | A | A | N |
| R | O | J | O | C | K | P | E | U | P | O | X | J | I |
| A | S | Z | T | K | M | N | N | X | E | R | U | K | A |
| N | A | C | K | E | V | I | N | B | N | D | F | H | T |
| G | C | H | A | R | M | C | A | S | T | E | R | E | P |
| U | T | C | A | T | D | V | A | E | D | M | A | L | A |
| F | C | S | E | V | E | N | S | E | V | E | N | T | C |

## Page 21

WEB TRAP – Trail d leads to the bad guy. The villain is a Forever Knight.

## Page 23

TOTALLY SWAMPED – There are 7 pictures of Swampfire and 6 pictures of Ultimate Swampfire.

## Page 39

ARMODRILLO ACTION – Pieces b, c and d are missing.

## Page 43

**NRG BLASTS** – There are 2 Knights left, in C1 and E1.

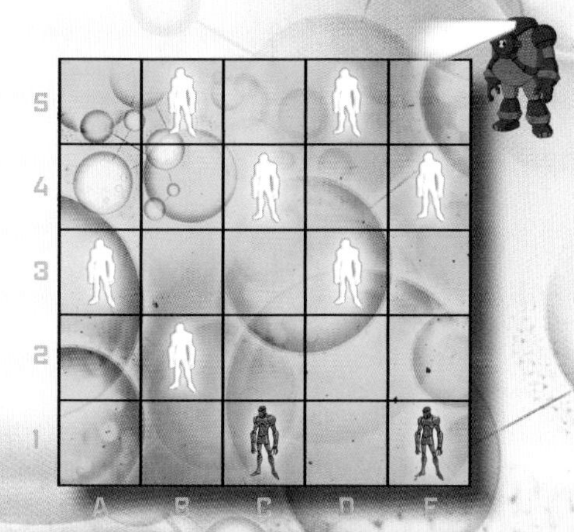


## Page 45

**TERRASPIN'S GRID**

## Page 47

**WATER CANNON** – a is 17, b is 18, c is 15. The most powerful route is b.

## Page 55

**RATH'S SPEECH** – Let me tell you something!

## Page 57

**AMPFIBI-MATCH** – Ampfibian would be best suited to the water in 'a' and he could sap energy from the power lines in 'c'.

## Page 65

**ALIEN SHADOWS** – a–3 (Ultimate Big Chill), b–5 (Ultimate Cannonbolt), c–4 (Ultimate Echo Echo), d–1 (Ultimate Humungousaur), e–2 (Ultimate Swampfire).

## Pages 66 and 67

**ULTIMATE QUIZ** –
1 – Ultimate Echo Echo, 2 – Let, 3 – Thunderstorm, 4 – Movie, 5 – Aggregor, 6 – Terraspin, 7 – Rustbucket III, 8 – X

The awesome Ben 10 object is the **Ultimatrix**.